A BODY AS STRONG AS A REDWOOD, LIMBS THAT EXTEND LIKE VINES, AND WITH THE
ABILITY TO REGROW FROM A SPLINTER...GROOT WAS THE BIGGEST AND STRONGEST MEMBER
OF THE GUARDIANS OF THE GALAXY. BUT NOW, HE'S STUCK AT THE SIZE OF A SAPLING. THE
GALAXY CAN BE A DANGEROUS PLACE FOR A LITTLE TREE WHO DOESN'T SAY ANYTHING BUT...

I AM GROOT

WRITER

Christopher Hastings

ARTIST

Flaviano

COLORIST

Marcio Menyz with
Rachelle Rosenberg (#2)

LETTERER

VC's Joe Caramagna

COVER ART

Marco D'Alfonso

EDITORS

Darren Shan & Kathleen Wisneski

CONSULTING EDITOR

Jordan D. White

GROOT CREATED BY

Stan Lee, Larry Lieber & Jack Kirby

COLLECTION EDITOR: **JENNIFER GRÜNWALD**
ASSISTANT EDITOR: **CAITLIN O'CONNELL**
ASSOCIATE MANAGING EDITOR: **KATERI WOODY**
EDITOR, SPECIAL PROJECTS: **MARK D. BEAZLEY**

VP PRODUCTION & SPECIAL PROJECTS: **JEFF YOUNGQUIST**
SVP PRINT, SALES & MARKETING: **DAVID GABRIEL**
BOOK DESIGNER: **ADAM DEL RE**

EDITOR IN CHIEF: **AXEL ALONSO**
CHIEF CREATIVE OFFICER: **JOE QUESADA**
PRESIDENT: **DAN BUCKLEY**
EXECUTIVE PRODUCER: **ALAN FINE**

Cale Atkinson
#1 NIGHT NIGHT, GROOT VARIANT

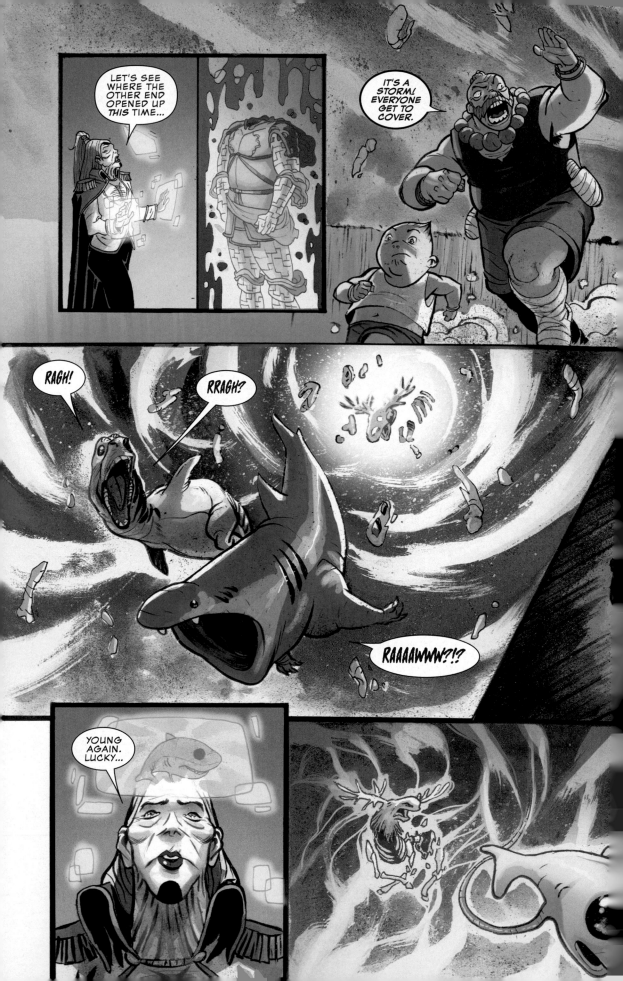

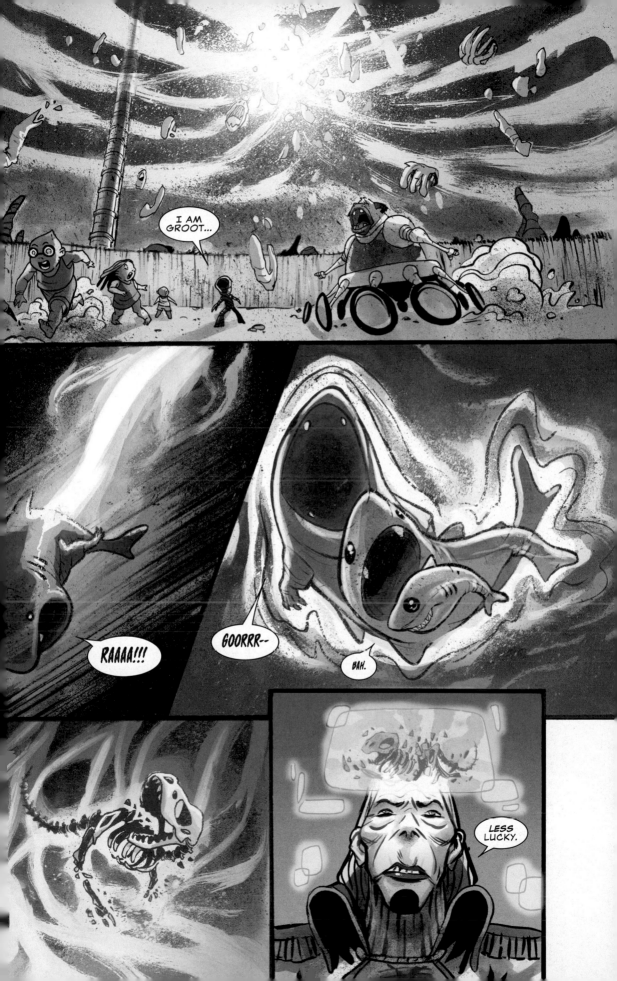

Jay Fosgit
#1 VARIANT

Greg Smallwood
#1 VARIANT

Theotis Jones
#1 HIP-HOP VARIANT

Nico Henrichon
#2 VARIANT

WE HAVE FAILED THAT LITTLE TREE...

REALLY GLAD I DIDN'T BRING THE KIDS FOR THIS NOW.

BUDDY, ARE YOU OKAY? YOU'VE BEEN QUIET.

OH, IT'S *AWFUL* THAT GROOT FELL IN THE STORM!

BUT, I GUESS IF I WERE TO SEE AN UPSIDE...

...HE WAS SURELY THE SEED OF SLAUGHTER FROM PROPHECY AND IT'S A GOOD THING HE WON'T BE ABLE TO OPEN THE DOOR THAT WILL DESTROY TERMINAL?

UH...

RMMMBLLE

ROGUE USERS ACQUIRED! RETURNING THEM TO BASE FOR ASSISTANCE!

"A HUB ACROSS GALAXIES. ACROSS UNIVERSES.